Preteen Edition

Henry T. Blackaby and
Mikey Thomas Oldham

Experiencing God

**Knowing
and
Doing
the
Will
of
God**

LifeWay Press
Nashville, Tennessee 37234

Table of Contents

Copyright © 1994 ▪ LifeWay Press
All rights reserved
Reprinted 1998; 1999; Dec. 22,
2000.
ISBN 0-8054-9859-1

Dewey Decimal Classification
Number J231
Subject Heading:
God–Will/Children–Religious Life

Printed in the United States
of America
Available from Lifeway Christian
Stores

Children/Preschool Section
Youth/Children/Preschool
Department
Discipleship and Family Group
LifeWay Church Resources
LifeWay Christian Resources of the
Southern Baptist Convention
127 Ninth Avenue, North
Nashville, Tennessee 37234

All Scripture quotations are from
the Holy Bible, New International
Version, copyright © 1973, 1978,
1984 by International Bible Society.

COME ALONG ON A JOURNEY

Welcome to the beginning of a very important spiritual journey—a journey where you will be challenged to experience God and learn how to know and do God's will in your life. On this journey we will be making seven stops. At each stop we will discover a new truth about experiencing God to put into your suitcase.

A journey with God begins when God invites you to walk with Him in all that you do. Jesus is our guide in our journey of faith with God. Under the master plan of God for your life, you will begin a relationship of love with God that is real and personal.

Every journey needs a good guidebook. Our guidebook is the Bible, God's message to us. Each week you will receive a "Spiritual Journey" sheet to take home. (Tear it out of this Scrapbook.) On it will be Bible verses to read each night along with some kind of activity. These activities will help you remember or understand the Bible truths. Reading your guidebook and praying each day are important parts of this journey. By doing both, you will be experiencing God right now as well as learning what you need to know to go further.

As we make each of the stops on our trip, we may talk, play games, make things, or do other activities in our Scrapbook. Another part of each stop will be "Snapshots". These stories-in-pictures will help you to further understand the truth at that stop. New places often mean new words that you may not understand. On page 40 in this Scrapbook is a "Travelers Word Book" with definitions for many words you may not know.

You will not want to miss a single stop on our journey. Every traveler likes to have a scrapbook in which to keep a record of the trip. This book is a scrapbook for your spiritual journey. Begin by writing your name on your ticket below.

Now your journey begins . . .

THE GOAL OF OUR JOURNEY IS TO EXPERIENCE GOD. IN THE PROCESS OF EXPERIENCING GOD WE WILL LEARN HOW TO KNOW AND DO THE WILL OF GOD. YOU WILL COME TO KNOW GOD IN A CLOSER WAY AS YOU EXPERIENCE HIM AT WORK THROUGH YOU.

- DOES GOD PREPARE CHURCHES TO HELP OTHER PEOPLE KNOW HIM?
- WHY DID WILLIE WANT THE DOLLS?
- WHY WAS THE UKRAINIAN GRANDMOTHER CRYING?
- HOW DID GOD USE THE DOLLS?
- HOW WAS GOD AT WORK IN WILLIE'S LIFE?
- HOW WAS GOD AT WORK IN THE CHURCH IN CENTER, TEXAS?

WHERE WE'RE HEADED

Following the example, draw a diagram of the seven stops we are going to make on our journey. Put a key word in each sign in a different color. Use the same color to fill in the word in the statements below.

THE SEVEN TRUTHS ABOUT GOD AND YOUR LIFE

1. God is always at _ _ _ _ around you.

2. God pursues a continuing love _ _ _ _ _ _ _ _ _ _ _ _ _ with you that is real and personal.

3. God _ _ _ _ _ _ _ _ you to become involved with Him in His work.

4. God _ _ _ _ _ _ _ by the Holy Spirit through the Bible, prayer, circumstances, and the church to reveal Himself, His purposes, and His ways.

5. God's invitation for you to work with Him always leads you to a _ _ _ _ _ _ _ _ _
_ _ _ _ _ _ _ _ _ _ that requires faith and action.

6. You must make major _ _ _ _ _ _ _ _ _ _ _ _ in your life to join God in what He is doing.

7. You come to know God by _ _ _ _ _ _ _ _ _ _ _ _ as you _ _ _ _ _ Him and He accomplishes His work through you.

ANY GOOD TRAVELER KNOWS AS MUCH AS POSSIBLE ABOUT WHERE HE OR SHE IS HEADED BEFORE LEAVING HOME. THIS WEEK, YOU WILL LEARN MORE ABOUT THE SEVEN STOPS YOU WILL BE MAKING. YOU DO NOT HAVE TO GO ALONE IN THIS JOURNEY; JESUS WILL BE YOUR GUIDE. HE WILL SHOW YOU HOW TO KNOW AND DO THE WILL OF GOD.

- WHY DID CHAD AND HIS MOTHER NEED MONEY?
- WHAT DID THEY DO ABOUT IT?
- WHAT HAPPENED?
- WHAT DID CHAD AND HIS MOTHER EXPERIENCE ABOUT GOD?

Read the Scripture passage for each day. Answer the questions. Unscramble the words to check your answers. Pray and ask God to speak to you through the passage.

(Note: The <u>New International Version</u> of the Bible is used throughout this study.)

Monday: Memorize the following Bible verse for Sunday:	"I am the vine; you are the branches. If a man remains in me and I in him, he will bear much fruit; apart from me you can do nothing" (John 15:5). What can you do without God? **G O H N T I N** _____
Tuesday: Read Genesis 12:1-5.	What instructions did God give Abram? **OG OT THE ALDN I ILWL SWHO OUY** _____ Are you willing to follow God by faith and not by sight?
Wednesday: Read John 5:17, 19-20.	Jesus is our example. What do these verses tell us about what the Son does? **NOLY HAWT EH ESSE HSI ATEHFR ODNIG** _____
Thursday: Read Matthew 20:26-28.	Why did Jesus come? **OT ERSEV** _____ Should you be God's servant? _____
Friday: Read 1 Kings 18:16-39.	What did God do? **NEST IERF OT SOCMUNE EHT SCIFARCI** _____ What did Elijah do? **BOEYDE ODG** _____
Saturday: Read Acts 4:13	Who did Jesus call to be his disciples? **YRODNIRA EMN** _____ Do you think God can use you? _____

Challenge Passages: (For those who wish an extra challenge)
Study the life of Moses using these passages:

1. Exodus 2:23-25
2. Exodus 24:12, 15-16, 18
3. Exodus 3:8, 10
4. Exodus 3:2-8; Numbers 12:6-8
5. Exodus 3:11, 13; 4:1, 10, 13; Hebrews 11:24-29
6. Exodus 4:19-20
7. Exodus 14:15-17, 21-23, 26-27, 29-31

JESUS' EXAMPLE

Jesus has promised to be our way. He has made the trip before, and He is the one that goes with us on this journey. He will show us how to know and do the will of God.

Use Jesus' words in John 5:17, 19-20 to fill in the blanks below.

"My Father is always at his work to this very day, and I, too, am working . . . tell you the truth, the Son can do nothing by himself; he can do only what he sees his Father doing, because whatever the Father does the Son also does. For the Father loves the Son and shows him all he does. Yes, to your amazement he will show him even greater things than these."

* The _ _ _ _ _ _ has been working right up until now.

* I, too, _ _ working.

* I do _ _ _ _ _ _ _ _ on My own initiative.

* I watch to see what the Father is _ _ _ _ _.

* I do what I see the _ _ _ _ _ _ already is doing.

* You see, the Father _ _ _ _ _ Me.

* He _ _ _ _ _ _ Me everything that He, Himself, is doing.

    Watch to see where God is working and join Him!

MATCHING:

The Seven Truths Shown in Moses' Life

Get a preview of each of our stops by looking at the life of Moses. Read each truth. Find the statements about Moses that match the truth. Put the letter on the line.

Seven Truths

____ 1. God is always at work around you.

____ 2. God pursues a continuing love relationship with you that is real and personal.

____ 3. God invites you to become involved with Him in His work.

____ 4. God speaks by the Holy Spirit through the Bible, prayer, circumstances, and the church to reveal Himself, His purposes, and His ways.

____ 5. God's invitation for you to work with Him always leads you to a moment of decision that requires faith and action.

____ 6. You must make major adjustments in your life to join God in what He is doing.

____ 7. You come to know God by experience as you obey Him and He accomplishes His work through you.

Moses' Life

a. God's purpose was to deliver the children of Israel. He invited Moses to be the one God would work through to deliver them. (Ex. 3:8, 10)

b. Moses obeyed God and came to know about Him through his experiences. (Ex. 14:15-17, 21-23, 26-27, 29-31)

c. God spoke to Moses through the burning bush. (Ex 3:2-8)

d. God heard the cries of the children of Israel as they were in slavery in Egypt. (Ex. 2:23-25)

e. Moses left Midian and returned to Egypt. (Ex. 4:19-20)

f. God spoke to Moses on Mt. Sinai. (Ex. 24:12, 15-16, 18)

g. Moses did not want to go to Egypt at first. (Ex. 3:11, 13; 4:1, 10, 13; Hebrews 11:24-29)

GOD IS ALWAYS AT WORK AROUND YOU.

GETTING STARTED. WELCOME TO YOUR FIRST STOP! AT THIS LOCATION, YOU WILL DISCOVER SOME IMPORTANT TRUTHS. YOU WILL EXPLORE THE DIFFERENCE BETWEEN GOD-CENTERED LIVING AND SELF-CENTERED LIVING. MOST IMPORTANT, YOU WILL DISCOVER THAT GOD IS ALWAYS AT WORK AROUND YOU. MAKE THIS TRUTH THE FIRST ONE YOU PACK IN YOUR SUITCASE TO TAKE ALONG WITH US.

GETTING THE PICTURE . . .

- HOW DID KAY FEEL WHEN HER FAMILY MOVED FROM OKLAHOMA TO JOPLIN, MISSOURI?
- WHAT DID SHE PRAY?
- HOW DID GOD ANSWER KAY'S PRAYER?
- HOW HAD GOD BEEN AT WORK EVEN BEFORE KAY MOVED TO JOPLIN?

Read the Scripture passage for each day. Use the code to figure out the coded word in each day's study. **CODE:** A C D E F G H I L N O P R S T U

Monday:

Memorize the following Bible verse for Sunday:

"Some trust in chariots and some in horses, but we _ _ _ _ _ _ _ in the name of the Lord our God " (Psalm 20:7).
Can you update this verse?
What do we place our trust in?

Tuesday:

Read 2 Chronicles 14:9-11.

King Asa's actions show _ _ _ _ - _ _ _ _ _ _ _ _ _ _ _ _ . He depended on God's abilities, not his abilities.

Wednesday:

Read Acts 9:1-16.

When we live a God-centered life, we focus on God's plans, not our own. When God starts to do something, He finds someone He can use. He appeared to Saul because God was ready to carry the _ _ _ _ _ _ _ _ to the Gentiles.

Thursday:

Read Psalm 81:10-14.

We need to change our lives so that God can do through us what He wants to do. If Israel had _ _ _ _ _ _ _ _ _ to God rather than their own hearts, He would have quickly taken care of their enemies.

Friday:

Read John 10:2-4, 14.

The key to knowing God's voice is not a method. It comes from a love _ _ _ _ _ _ _ _ _ _ _ _ with God.

Saturday:

Read Matthew 25:21.

We must be ready to follow God's leading even in small things. When God speaks to you is the moment he wants you to _ _ _ _ _ _ _ _ to Him. When you make Him Lord, you give Him the right to _ _ _ _ _ _ _ help Himself to your life anytime He wants.

Challenge Passages:

Read the following verses. Place an S before those that show self-centeredness and a G before those that show God-centeredness.

_____ God placed Adam and Eve in a beautiful and bountiful garden. He told them not to eat from the tree of the knowledge of good and evil. Eve saw that the fruit was pleasing to the eye and desirable for gaining wisdom, so she ate it (Genesis 2:16-17; 3:1-7).

_____ Potiphar's wife daily begged Joseph to come to bed with her. He told her he could not do such a wicked thing and sin against God. When she tried to force him, he fled the room (Genesis 39).

_____ After the 12 men went into the Promised Land to explore it and bring back a report, ten of the spies saw the giants and said, "We can't attack those people; they are stronger than we are" (Numbers 13:31).

_____ Joshua and Caleb said about the Promised Land, "If the Lord is pleased with us, he will lead us into that land . . . do not be afraid of the people of the land" (Numbers 14:8, 9).

_____ King Asa and Judah were being threatened by Baasha, king of Israel. Asa sent gold and silver to Ben-Hadad, King of Aram, asking for his help in this conflict (2 Chronicles 16:1-3).

HIGHWAY SIGNS

Divide today's memory verse, Psalm 20:7, into phrases and write each phrase on a sign. Then rewrite it in modern terms and put them in the second group of signs. Think about what we trust in today.

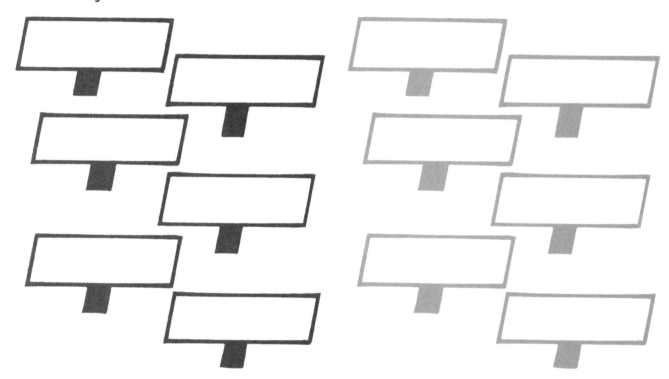

Psalm 20:7   In My Own Words

WHAT DIRECTION WILL YOU GO?

As you journey, you often will have a choice of a direction for your life. In Matthew 7:13 Jesus spoke of us choosing the narrow road or the broad road. Obey Jesus and follow the narrow road. Follow the guide, not the crowd!

Self-Centered Living

- Focusing life on myself
- Being proud of myself and what I have done
- Being self-confident
- Depending on myself and my own abilities
- Affirming myself (giving myself a pat on the back)
- Seeking to be acceptable to the world and its ways
- Looking at what happens from a human point of view
- Living in a selfish way

God-Centered Living

- Having confidence in God
- Depending on God and His ability and provision
- Living focused on God and His activity
- Being humble before God
- Denying myself
- Seeking first the kingdom of God and His righteousness
- Seeking God's point of view about everything that happens
- Living in a holy and godly way

GOD PURSUES A CONTINUING LOVE RELATIONSHIP WITH YOU THAT IS REAL AND PERSONAL.

CLIMBING THE MOUNTAIN. *HUFF, PUFF, PUFF. THIS PART OF YOUR JOURNEY BRINGS YOU INTO THE MOUNTAINS. DISCOVERING GOD'S CONTINUING LOVE FOR YOU CAN ONLY BE A MOUNTAINTOP EXPERIENCE. AND HIS LOVE FOR YOU IS REAL AND PERSONAL.*

GETTING THE PICTURE . . .

- HOW COULD TOM HAVE RESPONDED TOWARD GOD AFTER THE ACCIDENT?
- HOW DID TOM KNOW THAT GOD WAS STILL WITH HIM EVEN AFTER THE ACCIDENT?
- IF TOM WOULD HAVE ENDED UP WALKING WITH A LIMP, WOULD THAT HAVE MEANT THAT GOD DID NOT LOVE HIM?

Read the Scripture passage for each day. Answer the question or fill in the blanks. Then use the answer in the crossword puzzle.

Monday: Memorize the following Bible verse for Sunday:	"Jesus replied: ' "Love the Lord your God with all your heart and with all your soul and with all your mind." This is the first and greatest **5** _ _ _ _ _ _ _ _ _ _ _ _ _ ' " (Matthew 22:37-38). This verse tells us we are to first have a love relationship with God.
Tuesday: Read 1 John 4:9-10, 19.	How many times is the word **love** used? How did God show His love for us? **2** _ _ _ _ _ _ _ _ _ _
Wednesday: Read Matthew 6:19-21, 33.	God created you for eternity. You need to store up treasures in **3** _ _ _ _ _ _ _.
Thursday: Read John 6:44, 45, 65.	Who can come to Jesus without being drawn by the Father? **4** _ _ _ _ _
Friday: Read Luke 10:22, John 15:16, Philippians 2:13.	Use one of the following words to fill in the blank: **never, sometimes, often, always**. God **1**_____ takes the initiative (first step) to establish a love relationship with me.
Saturday: Read Mark 6:7-13.	The **6** _ _ _ _ _ _ _ _ _ _ _ had a real, personal, and practical relationship with Jesus—the Son of God. He did not send them out helpless. He gave them authority over evil spirits.

Challenge Passages:

Read these Scriptures which tell of a love relationship. Notice how many times the word love is used. A love relationship with God is more important than any other single factor in your life.

- Deuteronomy 30:19-20a
- John 3:16
- John 14:21
- Romans 8:35, 37, 39
- 1 John 3:16

A MESSAGE FROM GOD

Dear _____

_____

_____

_____

_____

_____

_____

Love, God

MEMORY VERSE MOUNTAIN SEARCH

Search through the mountains to find the words from this week's memory verse in the word search below. Words go right, left, up or down. Write the verse on the lines below. Use your Bible to check your work. Be ready to say the verse to your teacher.

```
W  R  L  L  A  G  B  G  R  S  G
I  U  A  L  L  O  S  O  U  L  R
T  O  C  N  H  D  A  L  O  V  E
H  Y  Z  Q  E  B  N  C  Y  D  A
C  O  M  M  A  N  D  M  E  N  T
A  U  I  Y  R  D  P  E  H  T  E
L  R  N  G  T  C  J  E  S  U  S
L  M  D  H  T  I  W  S  I  H  T
F  I  R  S  T  D  N  A  T  H  E
B  W  I  T  H  M  C  D  R  O  L
R  E  P  L  I  E  D  R  U  O  Y
```

Matthew 22:37-38 _____

_____

_____

GOD INVITES YOU TO BECOME INVOLVED WITH HIM IN HIS WORK.

CLEARING THE ROAD. *WATCH OUT! THE ROAD IS WASHED OUT! YOU WILL NEED TO HELP REPAIR IT BEFORE GOING ON. WHEN YOU SEE GOD AT WORK IN NEEDY AREAS, HE WANTS YOU TO HELP.*

- HOW WAS KAY GOING TO PAY FOR HER COLLEGE?
- WHAT DID THE FAMILY DECIDE TO DO WITH HER COLLEGE MONEY?
- HOW DID THEY DECIDE WHAT TO DO WITH THEIR MONEY?
- HOW DID GOD PROVIDE FOR KAY'S COLLEGE?
- WHY?

Read the following Bible verses for each day. Fill in the blanks using the words in the Word Bank. Some words are used more than once.

WORD BANK: good teacher ▪ inviting ▪ loves ▪ my friend ▪ hands ▪ good ▪ help ▪ provider

Monday: Memorize the following Bible verse for Sunday.	"Whoever has my commands and obeys them, he is the one who _____ me. He who _____ me will be loved by my Father, and I too will love him and show myself to him" (John 14:21).
Tuesday: Read Exodus 17:8-15.	God gave victory to the Israelites when Moses held up his _____ . Moses' uplifted _____ gave constant glory to God showing that the battle was His and Israel belonged to Him.
Wednesday: Read Genesis 22:1-18.	God asked Abraham to sacrifice his son Isaac to show his faith in God. But God showed Abraham that He was the _____ when He put a ram in a bush to be used for the sacrifice instead of Isaac. God was developing Abraham's character to be the father of a nation.
Thursday: Read verses	Hebrew names told a person's character and nature. Read these verses and write what name was used for God in each. Psalm 33:20 _____ Mark 10:17 _____ Job 16:20 _____
Friday: Read Deuteronomy 10:12.	God gives us commands for our own _____. Because He loves us, He wants only the best for us. If we love Him, we will obey Him.
Saturday: Read John 5:17, 19-20.	God takes the first step to show us what he is doing. If we are in a love relationship with God, we will see what He is doing and join Him there. When God shows us what He is doing, He is _____ us to join Him.

Challenge Passages:

A. Read John 14:15-17. If you love and obey Christ, whom will the Father give you? _____

B. Where will this person live? _____

C. Read John 14:26. What are two things the Holy Spirit will do for Jesus' disciples? _____
_____

D. Read John 16:8. What are three more things the Holy Spirit does? _____
_____

Practice saying these for Sunday:

1. God is always at work around you.

2. God pursues a continuing love relationship with you that is real and personal.

3. God invites you to become involved with Him in His work.

GOD SPEAKS BY THE HOLY SPIRIT THROUGH THE BIBLE, PRAYER, CIRCUMSTANCES AND THE CHURCH TO REVEAL HIMSELF, HIS PURPOSES AND HIS WAYS

LISTENING THROUGH THE CITY. AS YOU PASS THROUGH A CITY ON THIS PART OF YOUR JOURNEY, YOU CAN SEE MANY WAYS GOD USES TO REVEAL HIMSELF, HIS PURPOSES, AND HIS WAYS. YOU WILL NEED LOTS OF SPACE IN YOUR SUITCASE FOR THIS BIG TRUTH ABOUT GOD.

GETTING THE PICTURE . . .

- WHO DID GOD USE FIRST TO SPEAK TO MIKEY ABOUT JOURNALISM?
- WAS THIS PERSON A CHRISTIAN?
- HOW DID MIKEY LEARN ABOUT A CAREER IN RELIGIOUS JOURNALISM?
- CAN GOD USE ANYONE TO SPEAK TO US?
- DID MIKEY BECOME A RELIGIOUS JOURNALIST? (CLUE: LOOK AT THE COVER OF THIS BOOK.)

Read the Bible verses for each day.
Then write the missing word(s) in the statement.

Monday: Memorize the following Bible verse for Sunday.	"He who belongs to **1** __ __ __ hears what **1** __ __ __ says. The reason you do not hear is that you do not belong to **1** __ __ __" (John 8:47).
Tuesday: Read 1 Corinthians 2:9-12.	God speaks by the **3** __ __ __ __ __ __ __ __ __ __. An encounter with the **3** __ __ __ __ __ __ __ __ __ __ __ is an encounter with God. God speaks by the **3** __ __ __ __ __ __ __ __ __ __ to **8** __ __ __ __ __ __ Himself, His purposes, and His **11** __ __ __ __. God reveals Himself to increase your faith. He reveals His purposes so that you will do his work. He reveals His **11** __ __ __ __ so that you can accomplish His purposes.
Wednesday: Read Ephesians 6:17 and Philippians 2:13	When you read the **4** __ __ __ __ __, the Holy Spirit reveals the truth so you can adjust your life to this truth. When you obey Him, God can work through you to accomplish His **10** __ __ __ __ __ __ __ __.
Thursday: Read Romans 8:26-27.	God **2** __ __ __ __ __ __ to us by the Holy Spirit through **5** __ __ __ __ __ __. **5** __ __ __ __ __ __ is a two-way relationship with God, not just an activity. **5** __ __ __ __ __ __ is designed more to adjust you to God than to adjust God to you.
Friday: Read Luke 7:11-17.	God speaks through **6** __ __ __ __ __ __ __ __ __ __ __ __ __. The widow's **6** __ __ __ __ __ __ __ __ __ __ __ __ __ __ changed when Jesus came. Jesus is Truth. We cannot know the truth of what happens until we hear from God **9** __ __ __ __ __ __ __.
Saturday: Read 1 Corinthians 12:7-31.	God speaks to us by the Holy Spirit through the **7** __ __ __ __ __ __. We depend on others in the **7** __ __ __ __ __ __ to help us understand God's will and His **10** __ __ __ __ __ __ __ __ for our lives.

Challenge Passages:
Take your Bible study to a more serious level by following these steps using John 14:6.

1. Write down the verse in a journal.

2. Meditate on the verse. (Think about it for several minutes.)

3. Study it to really understand its meaning. What is God revealing about Himself, His purposes, or His ways? (You may need to look up some words so that you really understand what the verse is saying. You may need to find the verse in a study Bible and read any explanations given there.)

4. Identify the adjustments you need to make in your personal life, your family, your church, and your school so God can work that way with you.

5. Write a prayer response to God.

6. Make the necessary adjustments to God.

7. Watch to see how God may use that truth about Himself in your life during the day.

CONNECT-A-WORD

The first four truths are scrambled up in the city scene below. Use a different colored marker to connect each one. Then write each one on the lines below.

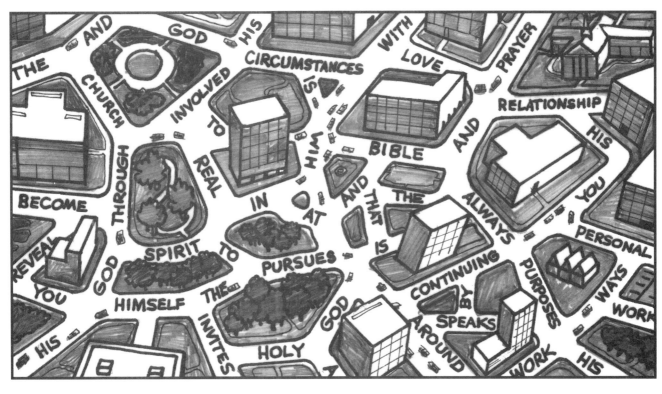

Truth 1: _____

_____

_____

Truth 2: _____

_____

_____

Truth 3: _____

_____

_____

Truth 4: _____

_____

_____

WHICH IS IT?

Read the situations below. Then number each one according to the way God is speaking by the Holy Spirit:

1. **Through the Bible** 2. **Through prayer** 3. **Through circumstances** 4. **Through the church**

___ 1. Jerilyn was selected to be on the school newspaper even though she had no experience. She discovered she was very good at it. Later she saw that God was leading her to write Sunday School literature.

___ 2. Terry was reading his daily Bible reading in Exodus 20. He had read the Ten Commandments many times. But this time when he read, "Remember the Sabbath day by keeping it holy," he felt that he should no longer play in ball tournaments on Sunday.

___ 3. Beth was praying. As she prayed, she thought of the verse, "Love your neighbor as yourself." She thought of Kim who was new to her school. She decided she should ask Kim to eat lunch with her tomorrow.

___ 4. The minister of music asked Carlos to take a part in the children's musical. Carlos had never acted. But he decided that if the minister of music thought he could do it, he should try.

GOD SPEAKS BY THE HOLY SPIRIT THROUGH THE BIBLE

Look at the diagram on the billboard above. Number the statements below in the correct sequence of how you encounter God by the Holy Spirit through the Bible.

_____ You obey Him.

_____ The Spirit of Truth takes the Word of God and reveals truth.

_____ You read the Word of God—the Bible.

_____ God works in and through you to accomplish His purposes.

_____ You adjust your life to the truth of God.

GOD SPEAKS BY THE HOLY SPIRIT THROUGH PRAYER

Look at the above diagram. Number the sentences below in the correct sequence in which you encounter God by the Holy Spirit through prayer.

_____ You adjust your life to the truth (to God).

_____ God takes the initiative (first step) by causing you to want to pray.

_____ You obey.

_____ You experience God just as the Spirit revealed Him to as you prayed.

_____ The Holy Spirit takes the Word of God and reveals to you the will of God.

_____ God works in you and through you to accomplish His purposes.

_____ In the Spirit you pray in agreement with the will of God.

_____ You look and listen for confirmation or further direction from the Bible, circumstances and the church (other believers.)

GETTING THE PICTURE . . .

- WHAT WAS THE MOMENT OF DECISION FOR JENNY AND HER FATHER?
- WHAT DID JENNY'S FATHER DO TO GET PATCH BACK?
- DID HE THINK IT WOULD SUCCEED?
- WHAT DID JENNY LEARN ABOUT FAITH? ABOUT GOD?

Read the following Bible verses for each day. Unscramble the words in each day's study.

Monday: Memorize the following Bible verse for Sunday:	"Without **aifht** it is impossible to please God, because anyone who comes to him must **evlebei** that he exists and that he rewards those who earnestly seek him" (Hebrews 11:6). _____ _____
Tuesday: Read Hebrews 11:1 and 2 Cor. 5:7.	**iahtF** is being sure of what we hope for and **taercni** of what we do not see. The opposite of **hitfa** is **gihst**. _____ _____ _____ _____
Wednesday: Read Matthew 17:20-21.	Faith as small as a **stdmaru edes** is all that is needed for God to do through you what is humanly impossible. _____ _____
Thursday: Read Mark 10:27.	When God speaks, He always reveals what He is going to do — not what He wants us to do for Him. Jesus said that what is **pbleimsosi** with man is **slipbeso** with God. _____ _____
Friday: Read Daniel 3:8-30.	God gives assignments that are God-sized so that the world will see Him at work. Only God could protect Shadrach, Meshach, and Abednego in the **erfiy ucrfena**. _____ _____
Saturday: Read 1 Samuel 17.	What you believe about God will determine what you do and how you live. David fought Goliath because he believed that God was a living God and was **eeldivrer**. _____

Challenge Passages:

When God invites you to join Him and you face a moment of decision, what you do next tells what you believe about God. Actions speak louder than words.

- Read Matthew 8:5-13. What did the centurion do to demonstrate his faith?
- Read Matthew 8:23-27. What did the disciples do to demonstrate their "little faith" in the middle of the storm?
- Read Matthew 9:20-22. What did the woman do to demonstrate her faith?

Be able to say these truths from memory:

1. God is always at work around you.
2. God pursues a continuing love relationship with you that is real and personal.
3. God invites you to become involved with Him in His work.
4. God speaks by the Holy Spirit through the Bible, prayer, circumstances and the church to reveal Himself, His purposes, and His ways.
5. God's invitation for you to work with Him always leads you to a crisis of belief that requires faith and action.

CHECK YOUR SUITCASE

Have you been getting every truth we've discovered into your suitcase? Fill in the blanks in the statements below to be sure you have them all packed.

Without _ _ _ _ _ it is impossible to please God, because anyone who comes to him must _ _ _ _ _ _ _ _ that he exists and that he _ _ _ _ _ _ _ those who earnestly seek him. (Hebrews 11:6).

1. God is _ _ _ _ _ _ _ at _ _ _ _ around you.

2. God pursues a continuing _ _ _ _ relationship with you that is _ _ _ _ and _ _ _ _ _ _ _ _.

3. God _ _ _ _ _ _ _ you to become involved with Him in His _ _ _ _ .

4. God speaks by the _ _ _ _ _ _ _ _ _ _ through the Bible, _ _ _ _ _ _ _, circumstances and the _ _ _ _ _ _ to reveal Himself, His purposes and His _ _ _ _.

5. God's invitation for you to work with Him always leads you to a _ _ _ _ _ _ _ of _ _ _ _ _ _ that requires faith and _ _ _ _ _ _.

MOMENT OF DECISION

The moment of decision is a turning point in your journey to follow God's will. God's will is for you to join Him in His work. When God gives you a God-sized assignment, you will see that you cannot do it on your own. The moment of decision comes when you have to decide if you will trust that God will help you do what He has asked you to do.

The Moment of Decision

1. **An encounter with God requires faith.**
2. **Encounters with God are God-sized.**
3. **What you do in response to God's revelation (invitation) reveals what you believe about God.**
4. **True faith requires action.**

Read the following Scriptures. Tell what the moment of decision is for each person. In other words, tell what each person had to believe about God to take action.

1. Joshua 6:1-5 _____

_____

2. Judges 6:33; 7:1-8 _____

_____

3. 1 Chronicles 14:8-16 _____

_____

4. Matthew 17:24-27 _____

_____

YOU MUST MAKE MAJOR ADJUSTMENTS IN YOUR LIFE TO JOIN GOD IN WHAT HE IS DOING.

TAKING A DIFFERENT ROAD. *GOD HAS LED YOU SAFELY ACROSS THE DESERT. NOW YOU ARE AT A CROSSROAD. GOD HAS TOLD YOU WHAT HE IS GOING TO DO. THAT'S HIS INVITATION TO ADJUST YOUR LIFE TO HIM AND TAKE THE ROAD HE DIRECTS YOU TO TAKE.*

31

- WHAT WAS GOD TRYING TO ACCOMPLISH IN BRAZIL?
- WHAT ADJUSTMENTS DID LORIE AND HER FAMILY HAVE TO MAKE TO JOIN GOD IN WHAT HE WAS DOING IN BRAZIL?
- HOW DID LORIE AND HER FAMILY PARTICIPATE IN WHAT GOD WAS DOING IN BRAZIL?

Read the Scriptures for each day. Then use the code to fill in the missing word or words.

CODE: A = 1 D = 12 F = 10 H = 3 J = 16 M = 9 O = 15 R = 8 T = 20 V = 14 Y = 21
C = 5 E = 2 G = 7 I = 11 L = 4 N = 6 P = 19 S = 13 U = 18 W = 17

Monday: Memorize the following Bible verse for Sunday:	"Any of you who does not give up __ __ __ __ __ __ __ __ __ he has cannot 2 14 2 8 21 20 3 11 6 7 be my __ __ __ __ __ __ __ __" (Luke 14:33). When God speaks to you, revealing 12 11 13 5 11 19 4 2 what He is about to do, that revelation is your invitation to adjust your life to Him. Adjustments prepare you for obedience.
Tuesday: Read 1 Kings 19:15-21.	Elisha's adjustment was to leave __ __ __ __ and follow __ __ __ __ __ __ 3 15 9 2 2 4 11 16 1 3 Because he followed God's call, God used him for some of the Bible's greatest miracles.
Wednesday: Read Acts 9:1-25.	Saul (later called Paul) made a major adjustment in his life. He went from __ __ __ __ __ __ __ __ __ __ Christians to telling others that Jesus 19 2 8 13 2 5 18 20 11 6 7 was the __ __ __ __ __ __ . 5 3 8 11 13 20
Thursday: Read 2 Corinthians 11:23-33.	Paul __ __ __ __ __ __ __ __ much for the cause of Christ. 13 18 10 10 2 8 2 12
Friday: Read John 19:17-37.	Because Jesus did the __ __ __ __ of God and died on the cross, His mother 17 11 4 4 paid the __ __ __ __ __ of seeing Him die a terrible death. 19 8 11 5 2
Saturday: Read Psalm 38:15.	We are to __ __ __ __ until we have heard a word of direction from 17 1 11 20 the __ __ __ __ . 4 15 8 12

Challenge Passages:

Read the following Scriptures. What kind of adjustment was required in each? Match the Scripture on the left with the correct adjustment on the right. Some may call for more than one type of adjustment.

_____ **1.** Matthew 4:18-22
_____ **2.** Matthew 5:43-48
_____ **3.** Matthew 6:5-8
_____ **4.** Matthew 20:20-28
_____ **5.** Acts 10:1-20

A. In circumstances
B. In relationships
C. In thinking
D. In commitments
E. In actions
F. In beliefs

Practice saying the seven truths.

TAKING THE RIGHT ROAD

Taking the right road means you may have to make changes in your life. The three statements on the road below give you clues on what these changes must be.

1. **You cannot stay where you are and go with God at the same time.**
2. **Obedience is costly to you and those around you.**
3. **Obedience requires total dependence on God to work through you.**

Read the statements above. Discuss with your group what they mean. Then write conversation for one of the scenes below as assigned by your leader. Determine who will play each part. Practice the scene and then present it for the whole group.

Statement 1 Scenes:

a. Oneta baby-sat all summer to earn money to buy a special outfit. Her friend Rahna was surprised when she did not buy it. Oneta explained that she felt God wanted her to give to the missions offering at church. (Oneta adjusted her financial plans to go with God.)

b. Dexter made fun of Chung Yun whenever he saw him. After a sermon on the Golden Rule, Dexter felt God wanted him to treat others better. He asked Chung Yun to sit with him on the bus. Dexter made an effort to get to know him better. (Dexter adjusted his attitudes about others to go with God.)

Statement 2 Scenes:

a. Starr went to a sleep-over at Heather's house. Heather started showing an R-rated video. Starr called her mother to come and pick her up. Wilomena became angry and never asked Starr to do anything with her again. (Starr's being obedient to God cost her because it meant she lost a friend.)

b. Hershel loved to play baseball and was the star of his Little League team. His coach started scheduling tournaments on Sunday. Hershel prayed and felt God did not want him to miss church to play baseball. He did not go to the tournaments. His team lost. (Hershel's being true to God cost him friends because they were disappointed by the loss.)

Statement 3 Scenes:

a. Rusty's cousin Laura who lived in another town was part of her church's puppet ministry in an apartment. Rusty thought it was a great idea. He talked with his RA leader and they organized one of their own. Few children came and in six months they canceled it. (Rusty depended on himself and others, not God for the idea.)

b. Lexxie noticed that the neighborhood near her church had many small children playing in the streets. She told her pastor about it and asked him about her organizing some games on the church lawn. Her pastor told the church and asked Lexxie and the church to pray about what to do. After praying, the people of the church decided God wanted them to reach out to these children. Several adults, youth, and older children joined Lexxie in volunteering to provide supervised play in the church recreation room each afternoon. Others volunteered to bring refreshments. The pastor said he would tell a Bible story each day. Soon many children and their families had been reached for Christ. (Lexxie and the church did not depend upon what they wanted to do, but asked God what He wanted to do through them.)

SAYING GOOD-BYE

Going with God on your journey may mean saying good-bye to certain things in your life. But God calls us to adjust our lives to Him. Match the following Bible people with the description of how each had to adjust his life to God.

____ **1.** Noah (Gen. 6)

____ **2.** Abram (Gen. 12:1-8)

____ **3.** Moses (Ex. 3)

____ **4.** David (1 Sam. 16:1-13)

____ **5.** Amos (Amos 7:14-15)

____ **6.** Jonah (Jonah 1:1-2; 3:1-2; 4:1-11)

____ **7.** Peter, Andrew, James and John (Matt. 4:18-22)

____ **8.** Matthew (Matt. 9:9)

____ **9.** Saul [Paul] (Acts 9:1-19)

a. Had to leave their fishing businesses in order to follow Jesus.

b. Had to leave his sheep to become king.

c. Could not continue life as usual and build an ark at the same time.

d. Had to completely change directions in his life in order to be used of God to preach the gospel to the Gentiles.

e. Could not stay in Ur or Haran and father a nation in Canaan.

f. Had to leave his tax collector's booth to follow Jesus.

g. Had to leave the sycamore trees in order to preach in Israel.

h. Could not stay on the back side of the desert herding sheep and stand before Pharaoh at the same time.

i. Had to leave his home and overcome a major prejudice in order to preach in Ninevah.

GETTING THE PICTURE . . .

- WHY DID THE CHURCH START A MISSION?
- WHERE ARE SOME OF THE PLACES THAT BECKY HAS SEEN CHURCHES MEET?
- HOW DID GOD PREPARE BECKY AND HER FAMILY TO HELP WITH THE MISSION?
- HOW DID GOD ACCOMPLISH HIS WORK THROUGH BECKY AND HER FAMILY BECAUSE THEY WERE OBEDIENT TO HIM?

For this final week of Experiencing God the daily Bible study will be different. Choose one of the truths or the Bible verse, numbered one through eight. Each day do the Bible study listed by the number of your choice.

Monday:	1. Exodus 1:6-10	5. Genesis 22:1-14
	2. Matthew 22:37-38	6. Genesis 6
	3. Luke 19:1-3	7. John 14:23
	4. Ephesians 6:17	8. John 15:4-6

Tuesday:	1. Exodus 1:11-12	5. Joshua 6:1-5
	2. John 3:16	6. Genesis 12:1-8
	3. Luke 19:4	7. Luke 6:46-49
	4. Romans 8:26-27	8. John 15:7-8

Wednesday:	1. Exodus 1:13-14	5. Judges 6:33; 7:1-8
	2. 1 John 3:16	6. 1 Samuel 16:1-13
	3. Luke 19:5-6	7. Luke 10:1-24
	4. Judges 6:21-22	8. John 15:16-17

Thursday:	1. Exodus 2:23-25	5. 1 Chronicles 14:8-16
	2. 1 John 4:9-10, 19	6. Matthew 4:18-22
	3. Luke 19:7	7. Matthew 21:28-30
	4. Exodus 3:2-8	8. John 15:1-2

Friday:	1. Exodus 3:7-9	5. Matthew 17:24-27
	2. John 15:16	6. 1 Kings 19:15-21
	3. Luke 19:8	7. Acts 16:6-10
	4. Ephesians 4:15-16	8. John 15:10

Saturday:	1. Exodus 5:6-13	5. Mark 10:27
	2. Matthew 6:19-21, 33	6. 2 Corinthians 11:23-33
	3. Luke 19:9-10	7. 1 John 2:3-6
	4. 1 Corinthians 12:7-31	8. John 15:11-13

Choices:

1. God is always at work around you.
2. God pursues a love relationship with you that is real and personal.
3. God invites you to become involved with Him in His work.
4. God speaks by the Holy Spirit through the Bible, prayer, circumstances, and the church to reveal Himself, His purposes, and His ways.
5. God's invitation for you to work with Him always leads you to a moment of decision that requires faith and action.
6. You must make major adjustments in your life to join God in what He is doing.
7. You come to know God by experience as you obey Him and He accomplishes His work through you.
8. "I am the vine; you are the branches. If a man remains in me and I in him, he will bear much fruit; apart from me you can do nothing" (John 15:5).

Which reality or Bible verse did you choose? _____ How will you illustrate it on the wall hanging?_____

SHARING YOUR JOURNEY

Travelers enjoy sharing memories of their journey with others. Sometimes they show slides or videos. Other times they tell stories. We are going to share what we've learned on our journey by making a wall hanging. On this wall hanging you will share each of the truths gained from each stop. So look into your suitcase and choose which truth you wish to share. Then follow these directions for making your square in our Experiencing God Wall Hanging.

1. Look at the sample square for ideas.

2. Discuss with your teacher the picture you have selected to use after doing your Bible study this week. You may wish to sketch your idea on the back of your "Spiritual Journey" sheet.

3. Draw and cut out the parts of your picture from construction paper.

4. Glue the parts on a piece of construction paper turned lengthwise.

4. Use a marker to print on the square the truth or verse you selected. The words can go over some of the picture if needed.

5. Punch holes around edge about 1 inch apart.

6. Take a doubled piece of yarn and go in and out the holes.

7. Glue the ends of the yarn down on the back.

8. Give your square to your teacher to glue on the paper backing.

CONTINUING THE JOURNEY

"I thank my God every time I remember you . . . being confident of this, that he who began a good work in you will carry it on to completion until the day of Christ Jesus" (Philippians 1:3,6).

We thank God for the work He has been doing in your life during the weeks you have spent in this Experiencing God journey. And remember the promise we find in Philippians 1:3-6: God will continue to work in your life for as long as you live. He wants you to continue to walk with Him during the rest of your journey of faith.

TRAVELER'S WORD BOOK

accomplish: bring about

adjustments: changes

affirming self: giving yourself a pat on the back

Christian: a person who has asked Jesus to be the Lord of his or her life

confess: agreeing with God about your sin

circumstances: things that happen

Moment of decision: a turning point when you choose whether to believe God will help you do what He has asked you to do

experience: learning that comes from things that happen

faith: belief in God

God-centered living: focusing on God and what He wants; living a holy and godly life; depending on God and what He can do through us

initiative: on one's own or first step

meditate: think about for a length of time

penalty: price required

provision: giving you what you need

pursue: go after

reality: truth about knowing and doing the will of God

relationship: the connection between you and God in which you learn about God's love for you and about God's ways

repent: turn from sin to God

righteousness: the result of a right relationship between God and a person; to do what is right by God's standard

respond: answer by doing what God wants

save: rescue from life without God

self-centered living: focusing on self and what I want; depending on what I can do; selfish living

sin: doing what you want rather than what God wants

spiritual markers: spiritual events in your life such as becoming a Christian

will of God: what God causes to happen

MY SPIRITUAL JOURNEY — PLANNING

Read the Scripture passage for each day. Answer the questions. Unscramble the words to check your answers. Pray and ask God to speak to you through the passage.

(Note: The New International Version of the Bible is used throughout this study.)

Monday:
Memorize the following Bible verse for Sunday:

"I am the vine; you are the branches. If a man remains in me and I in him, he will bear much fruit; apart from me you can do nothing" (John 15:5).

Tuesday:
Read Genesis 12:1-5.

What instructions did God give Abram?

OG OT THE ALDN I ILWL SWHO OUY _____

Are you willing to follow God by faith and not by sight?

Wednesday:
Read John 5:17, 19-20.

Jesus is our example. What do these verses tell us about what the Son does?

NOLY HAWT EH ESSE HSI ATEHFR ODNIG _____

Thursday:
Read Matthew 20:26-28.

Why did Jesus come?

OT ERSEV _____

Should you be God's servant?

Friday:
Read 1 Kings 18:16-39.

What did God do?

NEST IERF OT SOCMUNE EHT SCIFARCIE _____

What did Elijah do?

BOEYDE ODG _____

Saturday:
Read Acts 4:13.

Who did Jesus call to be his disciples?

YRODNIRA EMN _____

Do you think God can use you?

MY SPIRITUAL JOURNEY — STOP 1

Read the Scripture passage for each day. Use the code to figure out the coded word in each day's study.

CODE: A C D E F G H I L N O P R S T U

Monday:
Memorize the following Bible verse for Sunday:

"Some trust in chariots and some in horses, but we _____ in the name of the Lord our God." (Psalm 20:7).

Can you update this verse? What do we place our trust in?

Tuesday:
Read 2 Chronicles 14:9-11.

King Asa's actions show _____, not his abilities.

He depended on God's abilities, not his abilities.

Wednesday:
Read Acts 9:1-16.

When we live a God-centered life, we focus on God's plans, not our own. When God starts to do something, He finds someone He can use. He appeared to Saul because God was ready to carry the _____ to the Gentiles.

Thursday:
Read Psalm 81:10-14.

We need to change our lives so that God can do through us what He wants to do. If Israel had _____ to God rather than their own hearts, He would have quickly taken care of their enemies.

Friday:
Read John 10:2-4, 14.

The key to knowing God's voice is not a method. It comes from a love _____ with God.

Saturday:
Read Matthew 25:21.

We must be ready to follow God's leading even in small things. When God speaks to you is the moment he wants you to _____ to Him. When you make Him Lord, you give Him the right to help Himself to your life anytime He wants.

Challenge Passages:

(For those who wish an extra challenge)

Study the life of Moses using these passages:

1. Exodus 2:23-25
2. Exodus 24:12, 15-16, 18
3. Exodus 3:8, 10
4. Exodus 3:2-8; Numbers 12:6-8
5. Exodus 3:11, 13; 4:1, 10, 13; Hebrews 11:24-29
6. Exodus 4:19-20
7. Exodus 14:15-17, 21-23, 26-27, 29-31

Challenge Passages:

Read the following verses. Place an S before those that show self-centeredness and a G before those that show God-centeredness.

_____ God placed Adam and Eve in a beautiful and bountiful garden. He told them not to eat from the tree of the knowledge of good and evil. Eve saw that the fruit was pleasing to the eye and desirable for gaining wisdom, so she ate it (Genesis 2:16-17; 3:1-7).

_____ Potiphar's wife daily begged Joseph to come to bed with her. He told her he could not do such a wicked thing and sin against God. When she tried to force him, he fled the room (Genesis 39).

_____ After the 12 men went into the Promised Land to explore it and bring back a report, ten of the spies saw the giants and said, "We can't attack those people; they are stronger than we are" (Numbers 13:31).

_____ Joshua and Caleb said about the Promised Land, "If the Lord is pleased with us, he will lead us into that land...do not be afraid of the people of the land"

_____ King Asa and Judah were being threatened by Baasha, king of Israel. Asa sent gold and silver to Ben-Hadad, King of Aram, asking for his help in this conflict (2 Chronicles 16:1-3).

MY SPIRITUAL STOP 2 JOURNEY

Read the Scripture passage for each day.
Answer the question or fill in the blanks.
Then use the answer in the crossword puzzle.

Monday
Memorize the following Bible verse for Sunday:

"Jesus replied," "Love the Lord your God with all your heart and with all your soul and with all your mind." "This is the first and greatest ____ ." " (Matthew 22:37-38).

5 ___ ___ ___ ___ ___ ___

This verse tells us we are to first have a love relationship with God.

Tuesday:
Read 1 John 4:9-10, 19.

How many times is the word love used?
How did God show His love for us? 2 ___ ___ ___ ___ ___ ___ ___ ___

Wednesday:
Read Matthew 6:19-21, 33.

God created you for eternity. You need to store up treasures in
3 ___ ___ ___ ___ ___ ___

Thursday:
Read John 6:44, 45, 65.

Who can come to Jesus without being drawn by the Father?
4 ___ ___ ___ ___

Friday:
Read Luke 10:22,
John 15:16,
Philippians 2:13.

Use one of the following words to fill in the blank: **never, sometimes, often, always.** God 1 ___ ___ takes the initiative (first step) to establish a love relationship with me.

Saturday:
Read Mark 6:7-13.

The 6 ___ ___ ___ ___ ___ ___ had a real, personal, and practical relationship with Jesus—the Son of God. He did not send them out helpless. He gave them authority over evil spirits.

MY SPIRITUAL STOP 3 JOURNEY

Read the following Bible verses for each day. Fill in the blanks using the words in the Word Bank. Some words are used more than once. **WORD BANK:** good teacher ▪ inviting loves ▪ my friend ▪ hands ▪ good ▪ help ▪ provider

Monday:
Memorize the following Bible verse for Sunday.

"Whoever has my commands and obeys them, he is the one who ____ me. He who ____ me will be loved by my Father, and I too will love him and show myself to him" (John 14:21).

Tuesday:
Read Exodus 17:8-15.

God gave victory to the Israelites when Moses held up his ____ . Moses' ____ uplifted ____ gave constant glory to God showing that the battle was His and Israel belonged to Him.

Wednesday:
Read Genesis 22:1-18.

God asked Abraham to sacrifice his son Isaac to show his faith in God. But God showed Abraham that He was the ____ when He put a ram in a bush to be used for the sacrifice instead of Isaac. God was developing Abraham's character to be the father of a nation.

Thursday:
Read verses and write what name was used for God in each.

Psalm 33:20 ____
Mark 10:17 ____
Job 16:20 ____

Hebrew names told a person's character and nature. Read these verses and

Friday:
Read Deuteronomy 10:12.

God gives us commands for our own ____ . Because He loves us, He wants only the best for us. If we love Him, we will obey Him.

Saturday:
Read John 5:17, 19-20.

God takes the first step to show us what he is doing. If we are in a love relationship with God, we will see what He is doing and join Him there. When God shows us what He is doing, He is ____ us to join Him.

Challenge Passages:

Read these Scriptures which tell of a love relationship. Notice how many times the word love is used. A love relationship with God is more important than any other single factor in your life.

- Deuteronomy 30:19-20a
- John 3:16
- John 14:21
- Romans 8:35, 37, 39
- 1 John 3:16

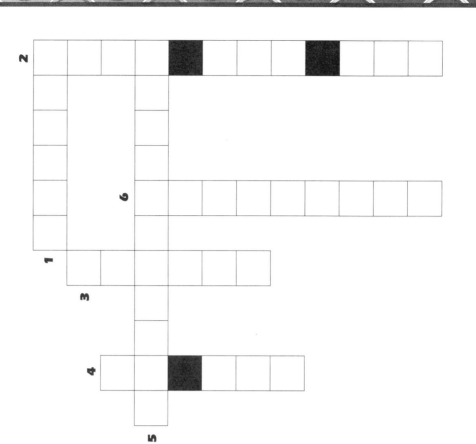

Challenge Passages:

A. Read John 14:15-17. If you love and obey Christ, whom will the Father give you?

_____

B. Where will this person live? _____

C. Read John 14:26. What are two things the Holy Spirit will do for Jesus' disciples?

_____

D. Read John 16:8. What are three more things the Holy Spirit does?

_____
_____

Practice saying these for Sunday:

1. God is always at work around you.

2. God pursues a continuing love relationship with you that is real and personal.

3. God invites you to become involved with Him in His work.

Read the Bible verses for each day. Then write the missing word(s) in the statement.

Monday: Memorize the following Bible verse for Sunday.

"He who belongs to 1_____ hears what 1_____ says. The reason you do not hear is that you do not belong to 1_____." (John 8:47).

Tuesday: Read 1 Corinthians 2:9-12.

God speaks by the 3_____. An encounter with the 3_____ is an encounter with God. God speaks by the 3_____ Himself, His purposes, and His 11_____ to 8_____ Himself, His purposes, and His 11_____. God reveals Himself to increase your faith. He reveals His 11_____ so that you can accomplish His purposes.

Wednesday: Read Ephesians 6:17 and Philippians 2:13.

When you read the 4_____ the Holy Spirit reveals the truth so you can adjust your life to this truth. When you obey Him, God can work through you to accomplish His 10_____.

Thursday: Read Romans 8:26-27.

God 2_____ to us by the Holy Spirit through 5_____ is a two-way relationship with God, not just an activity. 5_____ is designed more to adjust you to God than to adjust God to you.

Friday: Read Luke 7:11-17.

God speaks through 6_____ changed when Jesus came. Jesus is Truth. We cannot know the truth of what happens until we hear from God 6_____ The widow's 9_____

Saturday: Read 1 Corinthians 12:7-31.

God speaks to us by the Holy Spirit through the 7_____ We depend on others in the 7_____ to help us understand God's will and His 10_____ for our lives.

Read the following Bible verses for each day. Unscramble the words in each day's study.

Monday: Memorize the following Bible verse for Sunday.

"Without **aifht** it is impossible to please God, because anyone who comes to him must **evlebei** that he exists and that he rewards those who earnestly seek him" (Hebrews 11:6).

Tuesday: Read Hebrews 11:1 and 2 Cor. 5:7.

iahtF is being sure of what we hope for and **taercni** of what we do not see. The opposite of **hitfa** is **gihst**.

Wednesday: Read Matthew 17:20-21.

Faith as small as a **stdmaru edes** is all that is needed for God to do through you what is humanly impossible.

Thursday: Read Mark 10:27.

When God speaks, He always reveals what He is going to do—not what He wants us to do for Him. Jesus said that what is **slipbeso** with God.

Friday: Read Daniel 3:8-30.

God gives assignments that are God-sized so that the world will see Him at work. Only God could protect Shadrach, Meshach, and Abednego in the **erfiy ucrfena**.

Saturday: Read 1 Samuel 17.

What you believe about God will determine what you do and how you live. David fought Goliath because he believed that God was a living God and was **eeldivrer**.

Challenge Passages:

Take your Bible study to a more serious level by following these steps using John 14:6.

1. Write down the verse in a journal.
2. Meditate on the verse. (Think about it for several minutes.)
3. Study it to really understand its meaning. What is God revealing about Himself, His purposes, or His ways? (You may need to look up some words so that you really understand what the verse is saying. You may need to find the verse in a study Bible and read any explanations given there.)
4. Identify the adjustments you need to make in your personal life, your family, your church, and your school so God can work that way with you.
5. Write a prayer response to God.
6. Make the necessary adjustments to God.
7. Watch to see how God may use that truth about Himself in your life during the day.

Challenge Passages:

When God invites you to join Him and you face a moment of decision, what you do next tells what you believe about God. Actions speak louder than words.

- Read Matthew 8:5-13. What did the centurion do to demonstrate his faith? _____

- Read Matthew 8:23-27. What did the disciples do to demonstrate their "little faith" in the middle of the storm? _____

- Read Matthew 9:20-22. What did the woman do to demonstrate her faith? _____

Be able to say these truths from memory:

1. God is always at work around you.
2. God pursues a continuing love relationship with you that is real and personal.
3. God invites you to become involved with Him in His work.
4. God speaks by the Holy Spirit through the Bible, prayer, circumstances and the church to reveal Himself, His purposes, and His ways.
5. God's invitation for you to work with Him always leads you to a moment of decision that requires faith and action.

STOP 7

For this final week of Experiencing God the daily Bible study will be different. Follow the instructions given on the back.

Monday:
1. Exodus 1:6-10
2. Matthew 22:37-38
3. Luke 19:1-3
4. Ephesians 6:17
5. Genesis 22:1-14
6. Genesis 6
7. John 14:23
8. John 15:46

Tuesday:
1. Exodus 1:11-12
2. John 3:16
3. Luke 19:4
4. Romans 8:26-27
5. Joshua 6:1-5
6. Genesis 12:1-8
7. Luke 6:46-49
8. John 15:7-8

Wednesday:
1. Exodus 1:13-14
2. 1 John 3:16
3. Luke 19:5-6
4. Judges 6:21-22
5. Judges 6:33; 7:1-8
6. 1 Samuel 16:1-13
7. Luke 10:1-24
8. John 15:16-17

Thursday:
1. Exodus 2:23-25
2. 1 John 4:9-10, 19
3. Luke 19:7
4. Exodus 3:2-8
5. Chronicles 14:8-16
6. Matthew 4:18-22
7. Matthew 21:28-30
8. John 15:1-2

Friday:
1. Exodus 3:7-9
2. John 15:16
3. Luke 19:8
4. Ephesians 4:15-16
5. Matthew 17:24-27
6. 1 Kings 19:15-21
7. Acts 16:6-10
8. John 15:10

Saturday:
1. Exodus 5:6-13
2. Matthew 6:19-21, 33
3. Luke 19:9-10
4. 1 Corinthians 12:7-31
5. Mark 10:27
6. 2 Corinthians 11:23-33
7. 1 John 2:3-6
8. John 15:11-13

STOP 6

Read the Scriptures for each day. Then use the code to fill in the missing word or words in the statements for each day.

CODE: A=1, C=5, D=12, E=2, F=10, G=7, H=3, I=11, J=16, L=4, M=9, N=6, O=15, P=19, R=8, S=13, T=20, U=18, V=14, W=17, Y=2

Monday:
Memorize the following Bible verse for Sunday:
"Any of you who does not give up ___ he has cannot
2 14 2 8 21 20 3 11 6 7
be my ___" (Luke 14:33).
12 11 13 5 11 19 4 2

Tuesday:
Read 1 Kings 19:15-21.
When God speaks to you, revealing what He is about to do, that revelation is your invitation to adjust your life to Him. Adjustments prepare you for obedience. Elisha's adjustment was to leave ___ and follow ___
3 15 9 2   2 4 11 16 1 3
Because he followed God's call, God used him for some of the Bible's greatest miracles.

Wednesday:
Read Acts 9:1-25.
Saul (later called Paul) made a major adjustment in his life. He went from ___ Christians to telling others that Jesus was
19 2 8 13 2 5 18 20 11 6 7
the ___
5 3 8 11 13 20

Thursday:
Read 2 Corinthians 11:23-33.
Paul ___ much for the cause of Christ.
13 18 10 10 2 8 2 12

Friday:
Read John 19:17-37.
Because Jesus did the ___ of God and died on the cross, His mother
17 11 4 4
paid the ___ of seeing Him die a terrible death.
19 8 11 5 2

Saturday:
Read Psalm 38:15.
We are to ___ until we have heard a word of direction from
17 1 11 20
the ___ .
4 15 8 12

Choices:

1. God is always at work around you.
2. God pursues a love relationship with you that is real and personal.
3. God invites you to become involved with Him in His work.
4. God speaks by the Holy Spirit through the Bible, prayer, circumstances, and the church to reveal Himself, His purposes, and His ways.
5. God's invitation for you to work with Him always leads you to a moment of decision that requires faith and action.
6. You must make major adjustments in your life to join God in what He is doing.
7. You come to know God by experience as you obey Him and He accomplishes His work through you.
8. "I am the vine; you are the branches. If a man remains in me and I in him, he will bear much fruit; apart from me you can do nothing" (John 15:5).

Instructions for this week:

Choose one of the truths or the Bible verse, numbered one through eight. Each day do the Bible study listed by the number of your choice. Your study will prepare you for making one of the squares in the wall hanging next Sunday. The wall hanging will have a square for each of the truths and the Bible verse. Each square will be made by cutting out shapes to illustrate the reality or verse and gluing them on. Be thinking this week about how you will illustrate your choice.

Which reality or Bible verse did you choose? _____

How will you illustrate it on the wall hanging? _____

Challenge Passages:

Read the following Scriptures. What kind of adjustment was required in each? Match the Scripture on the left with the correct adjustment on the right. Some may call for more than one type of adjustment.

____ **1.** Matthew 4:18-22   **A.** In circumstances
____ **2.** Matthew 5:43-48   **B.** In relationships
____ **3.** Matthew 6:5-8   **C.** In thinking
____ **4.** Matthew 20:20-28   **D.** In commitments
____ **5.** Acts 10:1-20   **E.** In actions
                               F. In beliefs

Practice saying the seven truths:

1. God is always at work around you.
2. God pursues a continuing love relationship with you that is real and personal.
3. God invites you to become involved with Him in His work.
4. God speaks by the Holy Spirit through the Bible, prayer, circumstances, and the church to reveal Himself, His purposes, and His Ways.
5. God's invitation for you to work with Him always leads you to a moment of decision that requires faith and action.
6. You must make major adjustments in your life to join God in what He is doing.
7. You come to know God by experience as you obey Him and He accomplishes His work through you.